To my four brothers
A.B.

For Sarah B, Sara C and Sally F-K
C.G.

First published 1998 by Walker Books Ltd
87 Vauxhall Walk, London SE11 5HJ

2 4 6 8 10 9 7 5 3

Text © 1998 Alison Boyle
Illustrations © 1998 Cathy Gale

This book has been typeset in Gill Sans Bold Educational.

Printed in Singapore

British Library Cataloguing in Publication Data
A catalogue record for this book is
available from the British Library.

ISBN 0-7445-5577-9

What Goes Snap?

A First Book of Mix-and-Match

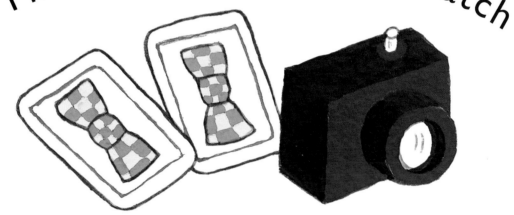

Alison Boyle
Illustrated by Cathy Gale

WALKER BOOKS
AND SUBSIDIARIES
LONDON • BOSTON • SYDNEY

One day, Penguin taught Squeak how to play Snap.

"We each turn our cards over, one by one," she said. "When you see two pictures that match, shout SNAP!"

But then along came Squeak's naughty friend, Spotty Dog, who took Penguin's set of cards!

See what Squeak and Penguin did next...

On Monday, Squeak found something that matched the stripy picture. Penguin took a photo.

What did Squeak see?
Can you see four other stripy things?

On Tuesday, Squeak found something that matched the starry picture. Penguin took a photo.

What did Squeak see?
Can you see four other starry things?

On Wednesday, Squeak found something that matched the flowery picture. Penguin took a photo.

SNAP!

What did Squeak see?
Can you see four other flowery things?

On Thursday, Squeak found something that matched the zigzaggy picture. Penguin took a photo.

SNAP!

What did Squeak see?
Can you see four other zigzaggy things?

On Friday, Squeak found something that matched the checked picture. Penguin took a photo.

SNAP!

What did Squeak see?
Can you see four other checked things?

On Saturday, Penguin and Squeak played with their cards and photos.

But when Squeak looked at his last card...

Then, on Sunday, Squeak saw someone who matched his last card!

Who was it?

His naughty friend, Spotty Dog!